LEARN AS YOU PLAY FRENCH HORN

BY PETER WASTALL

Revised edition 1990

Learn As You Play is a series of instrumental tutors designed specifically to prepare pupils for the early grades of all the principal examination boards. The tutors are suitable for both individual and group instruction.

The course, which is divided into 24 units, places the maximum emphasis on the early development of musicianship. From the beginning it introduces the student to a wide range of music, including works by leading contemporary composers. Each unit contains the following teaching programme:

1

New material is presented in clear progressive steps

2

Short, concise exercises enable new skills to be quickly developed

3

Instrumental solos by distinguished composers stimulate and develop practice repertoire

4

Progressive technical studies gradually bring the student into contact with specific instrumental technique

5

Instrumental duets (alternate units) provide experience in ensemble playing. Keyboard accompaniments to the duets can be added in early units

Progress is measured at eight unit intervals by the introduction of Concert Pieces which utilise all previously learned material

Piano accompaniments are available for these pieces in a separate accompaniment book. The Concert Pieces are works representative of examination requirements and in many instances are works which have been set in current or past syllabuses.

SERIES EDITOR
PETER WASTALL

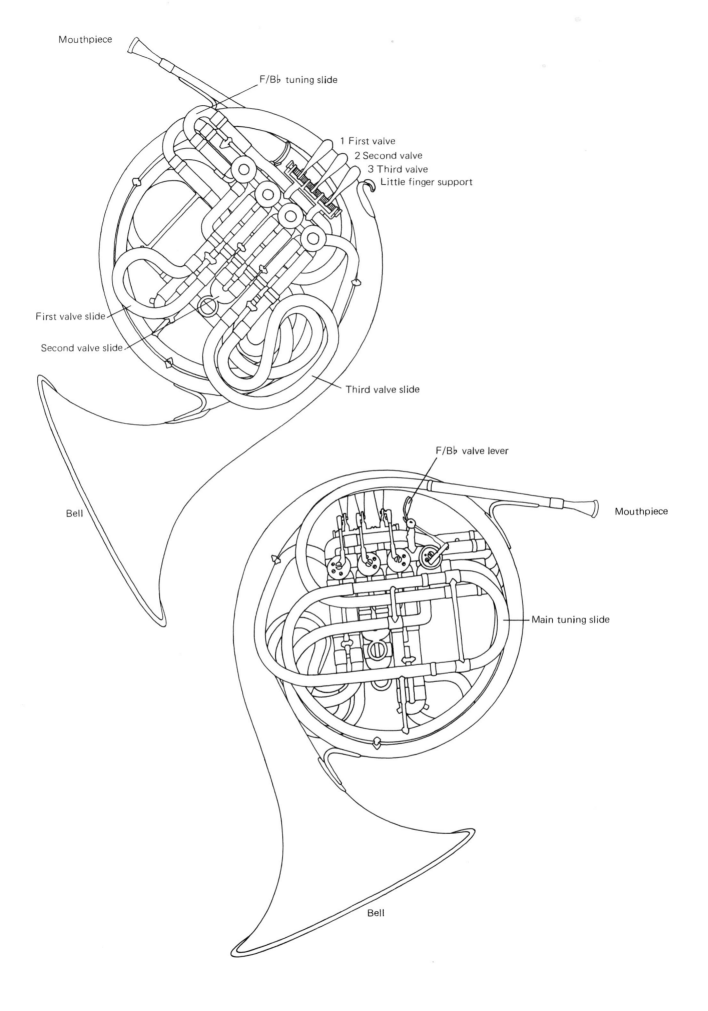

Mouthpiece

F/B♭ tuning slide

1 First valve
2 Second valve
3 Third valve
Little finger support

First valve slide

Second valve slide

Third valve slide

Bell

F/B♭ valve lever

Mouthpiece

Main tuning slide

Bell

Playing position

Usually, the bell of the horn rests on the right thigh, the bell pointing slightly away from the body.

Left hand position

Notice how the left hand little finger uses the little finger support, enabling the fingertips to be positioned over the valve levers. Pupils using an F/Bb horn should position the left thumb over the F/Bb valve lever.

Right hand position

Notice the angle and position of the right hand fingers (Pos. 1). Some players prefer the hand to be facing slightly upwards, however, the shape of the hand remains the same (Pos. 2).

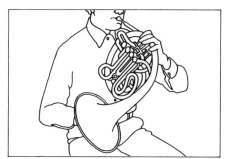 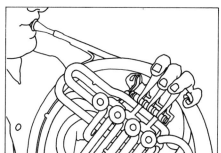 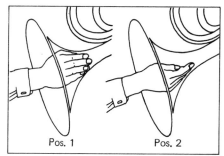

Mouthpiece placement

In most cases, the mouthpiece should be placed centrally on the lips, with two thirds of the top lip and one third of the bottom lip showing inside the mouthpiece when a visualiser is used.

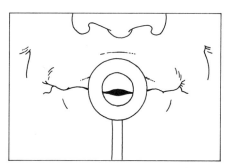

Open notes

In keeping with other brass instruments, the French horn has a range of notes that can be produced without depressing any of the valves. After producing the initial 'buzz', try to produce one of these open notes, starting on whichever is most comfortable to play. Usually a pupil's first notes are either C, E or G. The main objective will be to play E. If the first notes are higher than E, relax the muscles at the lip centre. If the first notes are lower than E, firm the muscles around the aperture. Once the E is established, relax down to the C and compare the embouchure formation required to play these two basic sounds.

Points to remember

1. Mouthpiece held lightly against the lips with just enough pressure to stop air escaping.

2. Cheek muscles firm (i.e. the cheeks must never be allowed to balloon outwards).

3. Jaw positioned so that both lips can vibrate freely.

After experimenting with the open notes, compare the sounds C, D, E and F.

Start each note with a tongue movement similar to that used when pronouncing the letter 'T'.

French horn pitch

The French horn is a transposing instrument, its notes sounding a fifth lower than the notes printed. Pupils using a piano to check pitch should play E on the french horn to sound the same as A below middle C on the piano. Pupils without a piano may find it useful to sound A on a pitch-pipe or tuning fork.

C	**D**	**E**	**F**
open	1	open	1

PREPARATORY MATERIAL FOR UNIT 1

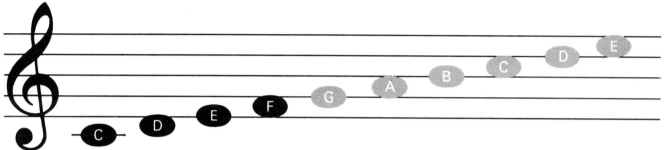

These are the notes shown in the fingering chart.

Notation

Printed notes are also named after the first seven letters of the alphabet. From the example it can be seen that they are placed on a staff (the name of the five lines), each line and each space counting as one letter name.

The Treble Clef

Since the same seven letter names are used for all instruments (i.e. those that produce high notes, as well as those that produce low notes) a clef sign is placed at the beginning of each staff to establish exact pitch. Music for the french horn is written primarily in the treble clef.

Note Lengths

The length of time a note is played is measured by the beat; the difference in length being shown by various types of note. The three types used in unit 1 are:

Play the following crotchets trying to hold each for exactly the same amount of time.

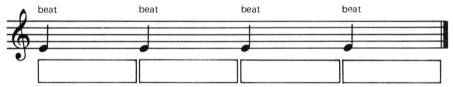

Now play the following minims, holding each note for the whole of beats one and two added together.

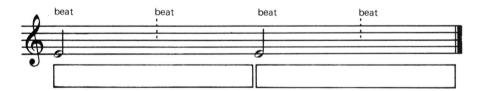

Now play a semibreve, trying to hold the note for exactly four beats.

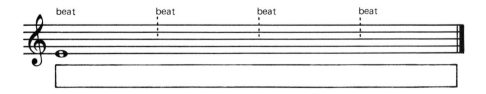

Bars and bar lines

	Bar line	Double bar line

Beats usually group themselves into regular patterns of either two, three or four; to show these patterns, the music is divided by bar lines into bars.

A double bar-line is used to separate differing sections of music within a single piece.

A thin/thick double bar indicates the end of a piece or exercise.

Time Signatures

A time-signature is placed at the beginning of each piece of music to show how many beats there are in a bar, and the type of note that equals one beat. It is printed in fractional form, the value of the crotchet being shown as a fraction of a semibreve.

2/4 showing 2 crotchet beats in each bar

1 2 1 2 1 2 1 2 1 2 1 2 1 2

3/4 showing 3 crotchet beats in each bar

1 2 3 1 2 3 1 2 3 1 2 3 1 2 3

4/4 showing 4 crotchet beats in each bar

1 2 3 4 1 2 3 4 1 2 3 4 1 2 3 4

UNIT 1

French horn pitch

written   sounding

Notes and Fingerings
(summarised from p. 2 – 5)

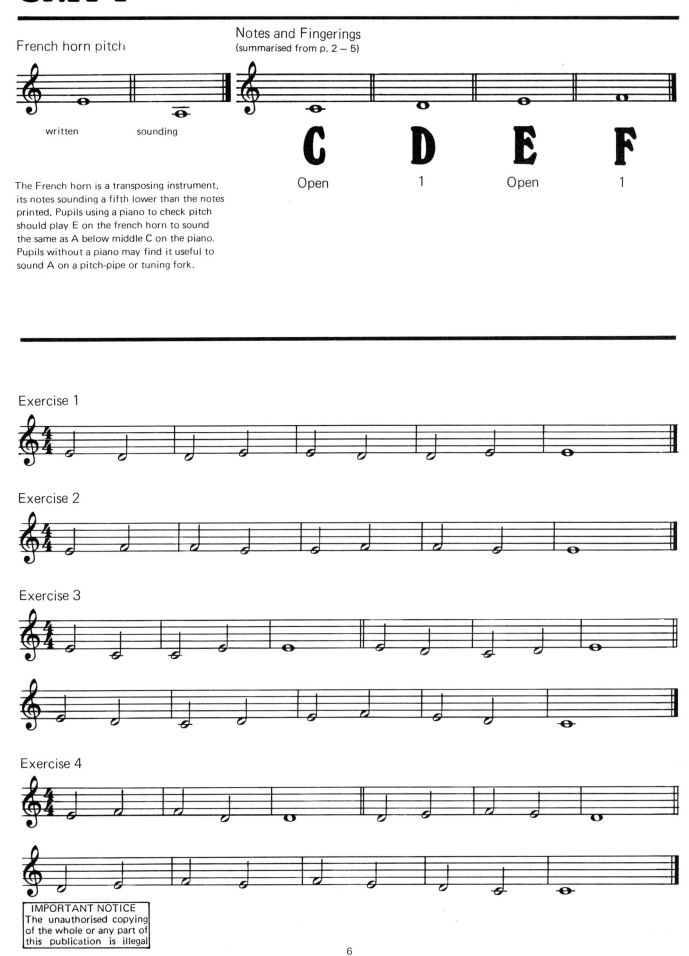

C   D   E   F

Open   1   Open   1

The French horn is a transposing instrument, its notes sounding a fifth lower than the notes printed. Pupils using a piano to check pitch should play E on the french horn to sound the same as A below middle C on the piano. Pupils without a piano may find it useful to sound A on a pitch-pipe or tuning fork.

Exercise 1

Exercise 2

Exercise 3

Exercise 4

Exercise 5

Musicianship

When you practise the instrumental solos, notice how the notes form patterns almost as if they were words in a rhyme. In music these note patterns are called phrases; to help to identify them, phrases in some early pieces have been marked with brackets. Breaths are normally taken at the ends of phrases; additional breaths can be taken, but these must be discreet so as not to disturb the natural flow of the phrase.

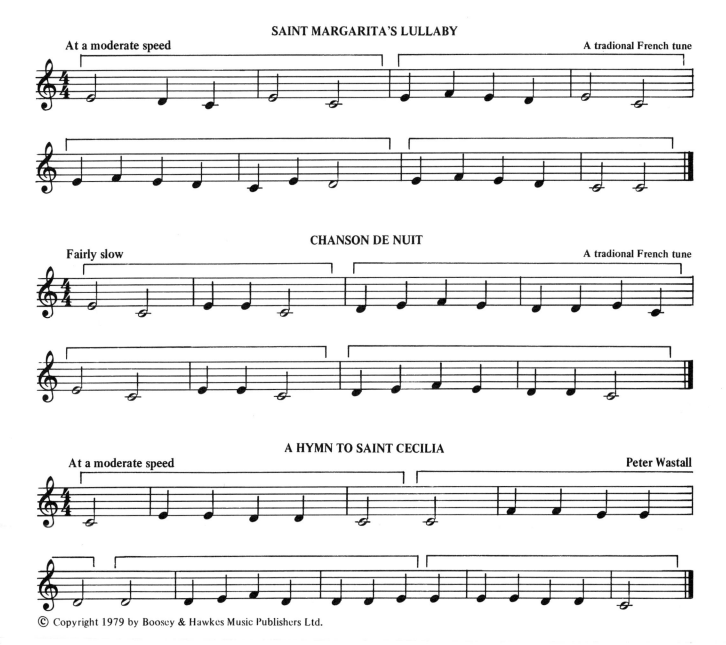

UNIT 2

The Pause Sign

Rests

When a pause sign is placed over a note, the beat stops and the note is played for a period of time longer than its printed value. During the first section of this book the pause will be used mainly in the exercises, identifying individual notes that are to be sustained for as long as possible.

The length of time in which notes are not played is shown by various rests, each note having an equivalent rest. The example shows the minim rest (two beats of silence) and the crotchet rest (one beat of silence).

Exercise 1

Exercise 2

Exercise 3

8

MINUETTO

Adapted from a minuet
by James Hook

Tone development

One of the best ways to develop a full tone is to play individual long notes. In the exercise that follows, listen closely to the sound and check these vital points.

1. Diaphragm giving a light support to the air stream.
2. Instrument held in such a position that both lips can vibrate freely.
3. Facial muscles firm, but not gripping.

LET'S BEGUINE
(A duet for pupil and teacher)

Peter Wastall

* Concert pitch chord symbols for keyboard accompaniment.

UNIT 3

New Notes

Dotted Minims

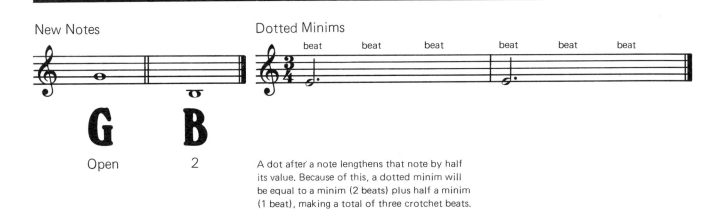

G Open

B 2

A dot after a note lengthens that note by half its value. Because of this, a dotted minim will be equal to a minim (2 beats) plus half a minim (1 beat), making a total of three crotchet beats.

Exercise 1

Exercise 2

Exercise 3

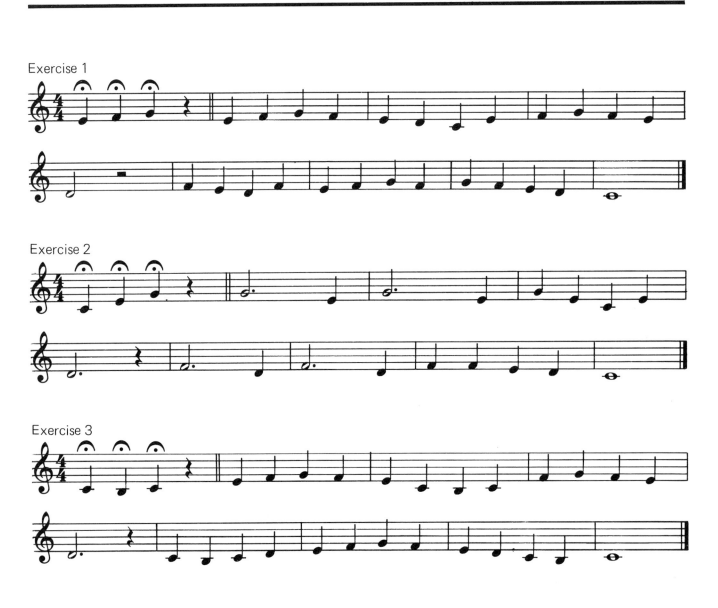

Exercise 4

Musicianship

The ability to remember melodic phrases plays an important part in the development of musicianship. To help develop a melodic memory, try each week to memorise one of the shorter instrumental solos.

The grade 1 aural tests issued by the Associated Board of the Royal Schools of Music will help memory development and should be incorporated into the lesson at this stage.

SWIM, SWAN, SWIM!

Lively

Derek Hyde

A LITTLE ETUDE

Fairly slow

Antonio Diabelli

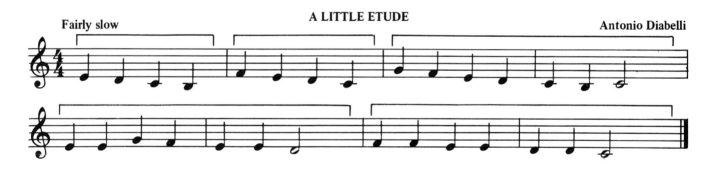

FFIGYSBREN

At a moderate speed

A traditional Welsh tune

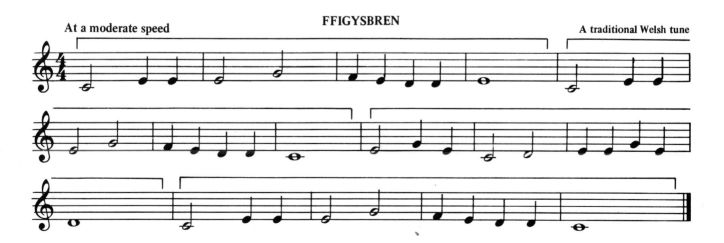

UNIT 4

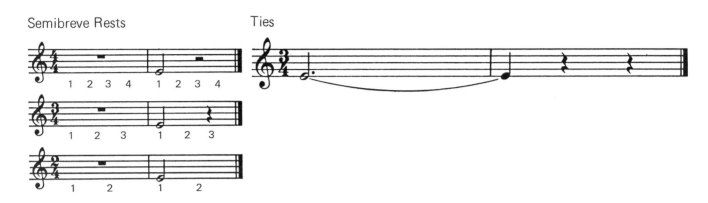

Semibreve Rests

Ties

A semibreve rest is used to show any complete bar of rest, regardless of the number of beats in the bar. When it occurs you must examine the time-signature to find the number of beats to be counted. Compare the three examples.

A tie is a curved line placed over or under two notes of the same pitch. The tie joins the notes together making one continuous note. In order to produce one continuous note, the second note must not be tongued.

Exercise 1

Exercise 2

Exercise 3

MARCH
"If all the world were paper"

In a bright march tempo

Adapted from a melody
by Derek Hyde

Tone development

1. Use exercise (a) for comparing the embouchure formation for playing open notes G – E – C.
2. Play each note with a relatively strong air pressure, keeping the diaphragm moderately firm.
3. Encourage the lips to vibrate freely, but keep the corners of the mouth in their correct position at all times.
4. Repeat the drill for each exercise.

MEXICAN MADNESS

Lively

Peter Wastall

Pupil 1
Pupil 2

UNIT 5

New Notes

A

1
2

Slurs

A slur is a curved line placed over or under notes of different pitch. It indicates that the notes contained within the slur are to be played smoothly in one continuous breath. In order to do this, only the first note is tongued.

Repeat Signs

When a section has to be played twice, a pair of dots is placed at the beginning of the section and another at the end. Used in this way the dots act as buffers, bouncing you back to the previous set of dots. When there is only one set, the repeat is made back to the beginning of the piece.

Exercise 1

Exercise 2

Exercise 3

CHORALE

At a moderate speed

A 16th century German melody

Tone development

1. Produce the upward slur by a small contraction of the embouchure muscles.
2. In bar 2, breathe through the corners of the mouth keeping the embouchure formation as still as possible.

3. Produce the downward slur by a small relaxation of the embouchure muscles.
4. Repeat exercise (a) using the notes shown in exercise (b) and (c).

"AH VOUS DIRAI-JE, MAMAN"

Fairly lively

A traditional French tune

A LITTLE PIECE

At a moderate speed

Robert Schumann

UNIT 6

Staccato Marks

Quavers

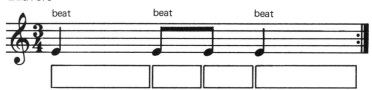

When a dot is placed over or under a note it indicates that the note is to sound detached. To achieve this, the note is played shorter than its printed value, often producing a clipped effect, rather like saying the word TAP.

The value of a quaver is half a crotchet: it is printed with a tail on the end of its stem. For ease of reading, groups of quavers usually have their tails joined together.

Exercise 1

Exercise 2

Exercise 3

BRANLE DE CHAMPAGNE

Fairly lively

Claude Gervaise

Aids to music reading

When you play quavers read them like a two-syllable word. For example, when you read the word 'Doctor', you don't read 'Doc' then 'tor', you read 'Doctor'. This 'block' reading skill should be developed at the earliest possible stage of music reading. To help this development, each time quavers occur, make a conscious effort to read both notes at the same time.

CORUMBÁ

Lively (in the style of a bossa-nova)

Peter Wastall

UNIT 7

New Notes

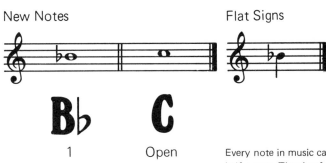

B♭   C
1   Open

Flat Signs

Every note in music can be raised or lowered half a tone. The sign for lowering a note half a tone is the flat sign shown in the example above.

Accent Signs

An accent sign placed over or under a note means that the note must be given a strong attack with the tongue. Often this strong attack is combined with a little 'punch' from the diaphragm.

Exercise 1

Exercise 2

Exercise 3

18

A MARCH OF JOY

Brightly

Adapted from a theme
by L. van Beethoven

Tone development

1. Play the first three notes quite firmly concentrating on accuracy of pitch. (Remember that the tiny muscles at the lip centre are the controlling factor.)
2. In bar 2, breathe through the corners of the mouth keeping the mouthpiece still.
3. Commence bar 3 with an embouchure formation identical to that formed at the beginning of bar 1.
4. Repeat exercise (a) using the notes shown in exercise (b) (c) and (d).

INTEGER VITAE

At a moderate speed

Friedrich Flemming

ARIA

At a moderate speed

Friedrich Gluck

UNIT 8

Keys and Key-signatures

*Because of the key signature, both these notes must be played as B♭.

Italian Terms

Keys and Key-signatures

When flat signs are placed at the beginning of each staff they are called a key signature. Each flat is placed on a specific line or space indicating that every note with that letter name is to be played as if the flat were against the note. The two keys that use the key-signature with one flat are: F Major and D Minor.

Italian terms describe how fast a piece is to be played and how loud or soft the music should sound. The terms which describe how loud or soft the music should sound are usually abbreviated. A table of the abbreviations is printed in Unit 12 where this aspect of technique is developed. A list of Italian terms is printed at the end of the book.

The two keys that have no flats (or sharps) in their key-signature are: C Major and A Minor. The duet in this unit illustrates music in C Major.

F Major

Exercise 1

Exercise 2

Exercise 3

RIGAUDON

Henry Purcell

Musicianship

Articulation (tonguing and slurring used in wind music) plays an important part in the creation of expression. It is the speech of music and can be thought of as the music equivalent of elocution. The tongue must be expressive, varying both the syllable formed and the strength of touch. In this unit concentrate on improving your articulation, using the pronunciation to give additional meaning to the phrases.

DUO
Adapted from "St. Petersburg"

Dmitry Bortniansky

CONCERT PIECES FOR UNITS 1-8

Piano accompaniments to the concert pieces are available in a separate accompaniment book. These should be used to provide experience in playing with an accompanist. 'Chorus' by Gluck, 'Romance' by Cole and 'Andante' by Gurlitt are examples of music that has been set for early grade examinations.

SERENADE
from "Twelve Short Pieces" op. 125

ANTONIO DIABELLI
(1781 - 1856)
arr. PETER WASTALL

CHORUS
from "Paris and Helen"

C. W. GLUCK
(1714 - 1787)
arr. PETER WASTALL

ROMANCE
"Homage to Peter Ilyich"

KEITH RAMON COLE

Molto moderato

ANDANTE
from "First steps" op. 82

CORNELIUS GURLITT
(1820 - 1901)
arr. PETER WASTALL

Andante

23

UNIT 9

New Notes

B
2

F#
2

Sharp Signs

The sign for raising a note by half a tone is called a sharp. Like the flat sign, it can be placed immediately before the note it affects, or it can be placed at the beginning of each staff to form a key-signature.

A New Key-signature

*Because of the key-signature, both these notes must be played as F♯.

The two keys that use the key-signature with one sharp are: G Major and E Minor.

G Major

Exercise 1

mf

Exercise 2

mf

Exercise 3

mf

A MELODY IN PHRYGIAN MODE
No. 28 from "Mikrokosmos" Vol. 1

Béla Bartók

Tone development

1. Use the first note to establish a good embouchure formation.
2. In bars 2 and 3, ensure maximum flexibility by using a minimum amount of mouthpiece pressure against the lips.
3. Pay strict attention to the slurs; even if a note fails to 'speak', resist the temptation to tongue it.
4. Repeat exercise (a) using the notes shown in exercises (b) and (c).

GERMAN DANCE

L. van Beethoven

ELLACOMBE

An English traditional tune

UNIT 10

A New Note

G

open

Dotted Crotchets

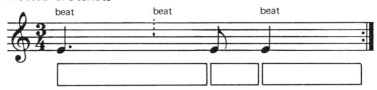

Since a dot after a note lengthens that note by half its value, the value of a dotted crotchet will be one and a half crotchet beats; the same length of sound as three quavers added together. Look at the example, then study the similarity of bars 2 and 3 in the second exercise.

Exercise 1

mf

Exercise 2

mp

Exercise 3

mf

26

THE EMPEROR OF GERMANY'S MARCH

Jeremiah Clarke

Tone development

1. Use this set of exercises to develop maximum vibration at the lip centre.
2. Check that the facial muscles are properly formed at all times, particularly the corners of the mouth outside the mouthpiece.
3. As you descend, gradually enlarge the mouth cavity by slightly opening the gap between the teeth.

FANFARE

Nicholas Chédeville

UNIT 11

New Notes

A New Key-signature

Accidentals

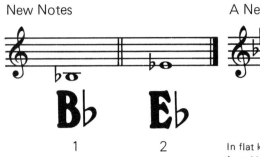

B♭	**E♭**
1	2

*Because of the accidental, both these
notes are B♭.

In flat keys, the name of the major key can be
found by counting four letter names down
from the last flat. The example shows a key
signature with two flats. Since the last flat is
E♭, the name of the major key must be B♭ Major.

When a flat or sharp is used that is not in the
key-signature it is called an accidental. An
accidental lasts until the next bar-line. Because
of this, it affects any note of the same pitch
that is left in the bar.

Exercise 1

mf

Exercise 2

mf

Exercise 3

mf

Scales and arpeggios

C major, to be played from memory.

Tone development

1. Use the rhythm of the exercise to help develop embouchure control.
2. Listen carefully to the sound and do not tolerate a pinched, nasal tone quality.
3. Breathe through the corners of the mouth, keeping the embouchure formation as still as possible.
4. Repeat exercise (a) using the notes shown in exercises (b), (c) and (d).

CRADLE SONG

Johannes Brahms

CONTREDANSE

Joseph Haydn

UNIT 12

Natural Signs

Italian Terms

pp	very soft
p	soft
mp	moderately soft

ff	very loud
f	loud
mf	moderately loud

— — — — gradually softer

— — — — gradually louder

A natural sign is used to cancel a flat or sharp. Since it is a type of accidental, it will only last for the bar in which it is printed. However, if a note that has been altered occurs again in the next bar, an additional accidental is often used to confirm that the note has returned to its original pitch.

Italian terms also describe the mood of a piece, changes of speed and large repeats such as da capo. As with Italian terms introduced earlier, English translations can be found at the end of the book.

A table of Italian terms which show how loud or soft the music should sound is printed above. It should be used in conjunction with the tuning technique introduced in this unit.

Exercise 1

Exercise 2

Exercise 3

A LITTLE PIECE

Moderato

Antonio Diabelli

Musicianship

Crescendos and diminuendos play an important part in creating expression but need careful use since they also have an effect on tuning. Basically, a crescendo (produced by increasing the air pressure) will make a note go sharp, and a diminuendo (produced by reducing the air pressure) will make a note go flat.

To stabilise the **tuning,** allow the lip aperture to open slightly during a crescendo, and close slightly during a diminuendo.

DUETTO No. 6

Andante

J. B. de Boismortier

UNIT 13

A New Note

C#

1
2

Quaver Rests

A quaver rest is a rest for half a crotchet beat.
Bar 1 of the example shows it occurring on the
second half of a crotchet beat, and bar 2 on the
first half. The rhythmic difference between the
two rhythms should be clearly understood
before playing their related exercises.

Exercise 1

Exercise 2

Exercise 3

Scales and arpeggios

G Major, to be played from memory.

Tone development

1. Start with a small accent, then concentrate on controlling the diminuendo.
2. Keep as still as possible during the first rest.
3. Commence bar 3 with an embouchure formation identical to that formed at the end of bar 1.
4. Repeat exercise (a) using the notes shown in exercise (b), (c) and (d).
5. Use the fingerings indicated in exercises (b) and (c).

ETUDE

Antonio Diabelli

COVENTRY CAROL

An English 16th century carol

UNIT 14

Compound Time

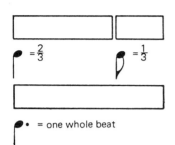

= one whole beat

Compound Time-signatures

When the natural pulse of a piece divides itself into thirds of a beat, the music is said to be in compound time. The various notes retain the same value in relation to each other, for instance there are still two quavers in a crotchet, but their value in relation to the beat is changed to the values shown in the example.

To show the new note values a new set of time-signatures is used. The example shows six-eight, indicating two dotted crotchet beats in a bar. A chart showing the complete range of compound time-signatures and how they are applied is printed at the end of the book.

Exercise 1

Exercise 2

Exercise 3

MARMOTTE

L. van Beethoven

Aids to music reading

When reading notes which are thirds of a beat, read them as if they were three-syllable words. As an example of this, try the first exercise thinking the word TENTATIVE as you play each group. When playing the pieces, apply this reading principle to all rhythmic groups contained within one beat.

DUO

François Garnier

UNIT 15

G#

2/3

Double Names for Notes

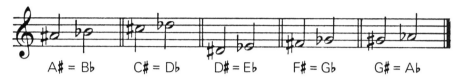

A# = Bb   C# = Db   D# = Eb   F# = Gb   G# = Ab

The interval between A and B is one whole tone. Since a sharp raises a note by half a tone, and a flat lowers a note by half a tone, it follows that A♯ and B♭ are different names for the same note. Double names can be given to all the flats and sharps learned so far.

Minor Keys

To find the name of a minor key, count three letter names down inclusive from the name of the major key. To find out whether the music is in a major key or a minor key, compare it with the appropriate scale.

A minor

Exercise 1

Exercise 2

Exercise 3

Scales and arpeggios

A Minor (harmonic form) to be played from memory.

Tone development

1. Produce the descending slurs by choosing just the right amount of controlled physical relaxation.
2. Remember that rests between the exercises are almost as important as the exercises themselves.
3. Repeat exercise (a) using the notes shown in exercises (b), (c), (d), (e) and (f).
4. Use the fingerings indicated in exercises (d), (e) and (f).

UNIT 16

Tenuto Signs

1st and 2nd time bars

A tenuto sign placed over or under a note means that the note is to be played with a lingering pressure. Usually it is also associated with a type of tonguing where one syllable is added to another without any noticeable break in the air stream.

Sometimes the ending of a repeated section is altered the second time through. When this occurs, 1st and 2nd time bars are used. The example is taken from "Ein' feste Burg" in which bars 1 - 4 are played quite normally the first time through, but when they are repeated the first time bar is omitted and the second time bar played instead.

Exercise 1

Exercise 2

Exercise 3

A chorale by M. Luther
adapted by J. S. Bach

Musicianship

Sometimes the general character of a piece suggests that many of the notes should be played staccato. When this occurs, the dots on top of the notes are often omitted, leaving it to the instrumentalist to interpret the music in a staccato style. The "Duo" by Chédeville is an example of this.

DUO IN E MINOR

Esprit Chédeville

D. C. al Fine

CONCERT PIECES FOR UNITS 9-16

As with earlier concert pieces, piano accompaniments should be used to provide experience in playing with an accompanist. 'Air' by Grétry is an example of music that has been set for early grade examinations.

PROMENADE

Jaunty and fairly fast

DEREK HYDE

AIR

from "Richard Coeur de Lion"

ANDRE GRETRY
(1741 - 1813)
arr. PETER WASTALL

Moderato

CONCERT PIECE
from *"Method for the natural horn" (1802)*

FREDERIC DUVERNOY
(1765 - 1838)
Keyboard realisation by
KEITH RAMON COLE

UNIT 17

A New Note

D

Open

B♭ fingering *

1
2

Grace Notes

In their simplest form, grace notes are notes added to a melody to make the music sound more decorative. To show how they are used, first play the example without the pair of grace notes, then again, using the grace notes to decorate the second A. As a general rule, grace notes should be played gracefully and lightly.

*Change to B♭ horn by depressing the F/B♭ valve lever with the left thumb.

STUDY No. 1
from 'Method for the Horn', op.21

Hippolyte Niessel

ON WINGS OF SONG

F. Mendelssohn

Andante tranquillo

F/B♭ technique

1. The notes G♯, A, B♭, B and C are fingered the same on both horns. Phrases such as exercise (a) will sound well on either and should be practised first on the F horn, then on the B♭ horn (see also bars 13 and 14 of "Andante" by Gabrielsky).

2. Because of its greater accuracy in the higher register phrases such as exercise (b) are usually played on the B♭ horn (see also bars 5 — 7 of "Andante" by Gabrielsky).

3. In phrases such as exercise (c) the switch to B♭ horn is made on one of the boxed notes. In scale passages, most players change on either A or D so that the switch is preceded or followed by an open fingering.

ANDANTE

Andante

Johann Gabrielsky

D. C. al Fine

UNIT 18

Semiquavers

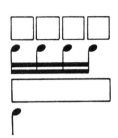

Syncopation

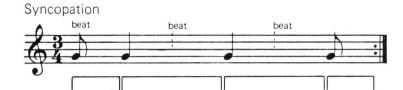

The value of a semiquaver is a quarter of a crotchet; it is printed with two tails on the end of its stem. As with quavers, all the tails contained in one beat can be joined together.

A new rhythm, called syncopation, is produced when strongly accented notes occur between the beats instead of coinciding with them.

As shown in the duet, the surrounding quavers are usually played staccato to help bounce the syncopated notes off the beat.

Exercise 1

Exercise 2

Scales and arpeggios

Bb Major, to be played from memory.

LARGHETTO

W. A. Mozart

Aids to music reading

With blocks of four semiquavers, read each group as you would a four-syllable word. Start with passages that are easy to play (such as the two exercises shown opposite) and make a conscious effort to read each block of four semiquavers as a single unit.

A SYNCOPATED DUET

François Garnier

UNIT 19

A New Note

C#

2

B♭ fingering

2
3

Dotted Quavers

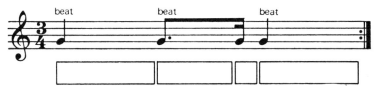

A dotted quaver, or its equivalent rest, lasts for three quarters of a crotchet beat, Usually it is combined with a single semiquaver since this completes the beat.

STUDY No. 2
from 'Method for the Horn', op.21

Hippolyte Niessel

46

St. ANTHONY CHORALE

Joseph Haydn

Aids to music reading

The reading technique for a single semiquaver is to group the semiquaver with the note which follows. In lively movements, a useful way to achieve this is to pronounce the two notes as if saying the word TODAY. As an example, play the first note of the "Soldier's March" by Schumann, then think TODAY as you play the next two notes. This reading technique can be used every time a dotted rhythm occurs.

SOLDIER'S MARCH

R. Schumann

UNIT 20

Semiquaver Rests

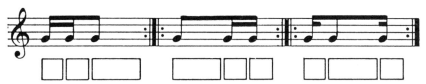

Note patterns using Semiquavers

A semiquaver rest is a rest for a quarter of a crotchet beat. Notice that it is similar to the semiquaver note, being printed with two tails. Examples of the semiquaver rest can be found in the duet.

By combining semiquavers with quavers, several new rhythm patterns can be formed. The examples should be studied carefully before playing the exercises.

Exercise 1

Exercise 2

Scales and arpeggios

D Minor (harmonic form) to be played from memory.

48

SHORE'S TRUMPET TUNE

From an eighteenth century
collection of trumpet tunes

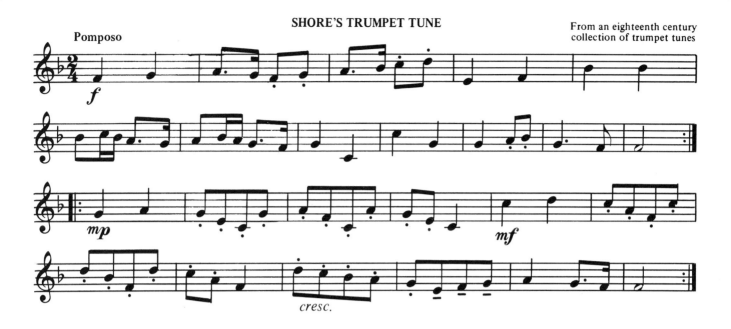

Musicianship

As you play the "Duetto" by Devienne, notice that the general character is one of smoothness. To achieve this smoothness, use a very gentle type of tonguing; rather like pronouncing the syllable DAH. When playing in this manner, we say we are interpreting the music in a legato style. Compare the style with that needed for playing "Shore's trumpet tune", where the mood demands that a vigorous, accented type of tonguing be used.

DUETTO

F. Devienne

UNIT 21

A New Note

Eb

2

Bb fingering

1

Three-eight Time

The time-signature of three-eight indicates that there are three quaver beats in each bar. As before, the various notes retain the same value in relation to each other; it is the value of the notes in relation to the beat that is changed.

STUDY No. 3
from 'Method for the Horn', op.21

Hippolyte Niessel

SARABANDE

Largo

Arcangelo Corelli

Tone development

1. Use these exercises to help develop upper register playing on the F horn. USE F HORN THROUGHOUT.
2. Play bars 1 and 2 with a fairly strong air pressure and then concentrate on controlling the diminuendo.
3. When playing bar 3, remember: diaphram; minimum mouthpiece pressure; mental awareness of the tiny muscles at the lip centre. These are the control points for accurate pitch.
4. Repeat exercise (a) through the various valve combinations starting on the notes shown. Use the fingerings indicated in exercises (d), (e) and (f).

SERENADE

Adapted from a
Feld-parthie by Joseph Haydn

UNIT 22

Acciaccaturas

Three-two Time

An acciaccatura is a small grace note with a stroke through its stem. It should be played on the beat and as short as possible.

The time signature of three-two indicates that there are three minim beats in each bar. The value of the notes in relation to the beat is shown in the example.

Exercise 1

Frédéric Duvernoy

Scales and arpeggios

D Major, to be played from memory.

B Minor (harmonic form), to be played from memory.

G Minor (harmonic form), to be played from memory

GAGLIARDA

Girolamo Frescobaldi

F/B♭ technique

1. Use these exercises to help develop middle register playing on the B♭ horn. USE B♭ HORN THROUGHOUT.

2. For downward slurs (notes 2 and 4), enlarge the mouth cavity by slightly opening the gap between the teeth.

3. For upward slurs (notes 3 and 5), help the embouchure contraction by giving a little extra support from the diaphragm.

4. As before, repeat exercise (a) using the fingerings indicated.

MINUET

W. A. Mozart

UNIT 23

A New Note

E

Open

B♭ fingering

2

Change of Time signature

Sometimes a time-signature is changed during the course of a piece. When this occurs the speed of the beat usually remains the same; it is the pulse pattern that changes. The example is taken from the "Cantilena" by Árpad Balázs.

STUDY No. 4
from 'Method for the Horn', op.21

Hippolyte Niessel

CANTILENA
from "Piano Miniatures for Children"

Árpád Balázs
(b. 1937)

Molto legato

mf espress.

poco a poco dim.

rall.

Tone development

1. Use these exercises to continue the development of upper register playing on the F horn. USE F HORN THROUGHOUT.
2. As before, play bars 1 and 2 with a fairly strong air pressure, then concentrate on controlling the diminuendo.

3. In bar 3, the notes must be produced by sensitive control of the embouchure muscles. It is important to memorise the muscular 'feel' of these notes.
4. Repeat exercise (a) through each valve combination, starting on the notes shown.

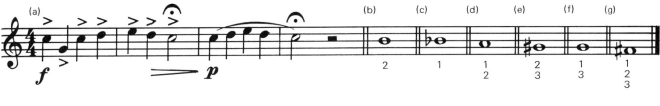

THIRD MODE MELODY

Largo

Thomas Tallis

mf

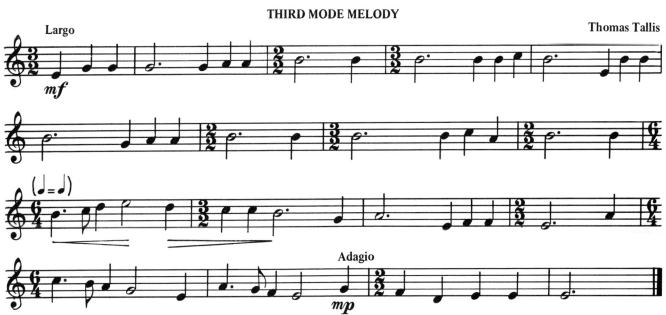

$(\ \bullet = \bullet\ )$

Adagio

mp

Triplets

Rests of Several Bars

1	2 (1st bar)
2	2 (2nd bar)
3	2 (3rd bar)
etc.	

A triplet can be defined as 'three notes played in the time of two notes of the same value' (for instance, three quavers played in the time of two quavers). The number 3 is placed over or under them to show the momentary change of note value.

When a rest of several bars is required, only one bar is used, a black line is usually drawn in this bar, and the number of complete bars to be counted placed on top. The example is taken from the concert piece on p.60.

Exercise 1

Wilhelm Popp

Scales and arpeggios

G Major, to be played from memory.

E Minor (harmonic form) to be played from memory.

A Major, to be played from memory.

ARIA

G. F. Handel

Musicianship

Both pieces in this unit have performing directions relating to their mood: the Handel "Aria" is marked dolce espressivo, and the Mozart "Minuet" grazioso. As you practise, try to create these moods, and in particular use the shapes of the phrases for displaying control over the dynamics. In the "Aria", the repeated notes create good opportunities for expressive tenuto playing; the important thing to remember is that performing directions are a starting point for creating your own expression.

MINUET

W. A. Mozart

CONCERT PIECES FOR UNITS 17-24

'Entr'acte' by Schubert, 'Quick Dance' by
Bogar and 'Canzonetta' by Pergolesi are
examples of music that has been set for
early grade examinations.

SOLSTICE

KEITH RAMON COLE

Poco lento

mf (misterioso)

LULLABY

ROBERT SCHUMANN
(1810 - 1856)
arr. PETER WASTALL

Moderato

ENTR'ACTE

from "Rosamunde"

FRANZ SCHUBERT
(1797 - 1828)
arr. PETER WASTALL

QUICK DANCE
from "Horn Music for Beginners"

ISTVÁN BOGÁR
(b. 1937)

© 1972 by Editio Musica, Budapest

SOLILOQUY

DEREK HYDE

CANZONETTA
"Tre giorni son che Nina"

GIOVANNI PERGOLESI
(1710 - 1736)
arr. PETER WASTALL

BASIC FINGERING CHART

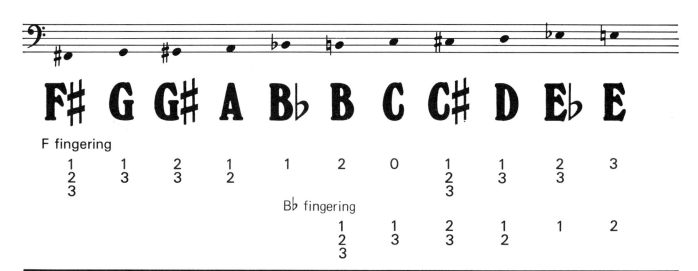

	F#	G	G#	A	Bb	B	C	C#	D	Eb	E
F fingering	1 2 3	1 3	2 3	1 2	1	2	0	1 2 3	1 3	2 3	3
Bb fingering						1 2 3	1 3	2 3	1 2	1	2

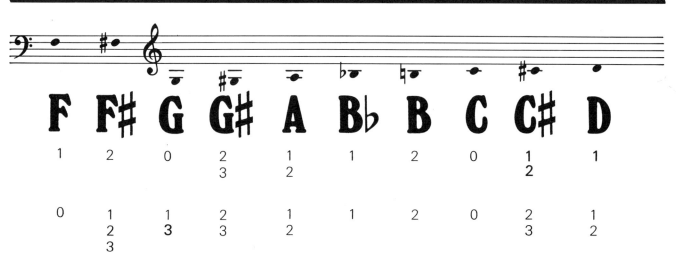

F	F#	G	G#	A	Bb	B	C	C#	D
1	2	0	2 3	1 2	1	2	0	**1 2**	1
0	1 2 3	1 **3**	2 3	1 2	1	2	0	2 3	1 2

Eb	E	F	F#	G	G#	A	Bb	B	C	C#
2	0	1	2	0	2 3	1 2	1	2	0	**2**
1	2	0	1 2	1	2 3	1 2	1	2	0	2 3

D	E♭	E	F	F♯	G	G♯	A	B♭	B	C
0	2	0	1	2	0	2 3	1 2	1	2	0
1 2	1	2	0	2	0	2 3	1 2	1	2	0

F horn - Basic notes available from each valve combination

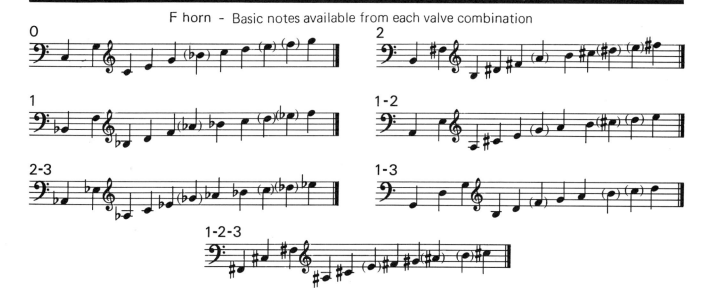

B♭ horn - Basic notes available from each valve combination

TIME SIGNATURES

1. Look up the time signature

2. Look in the left hand column to find the number of beats in each bar.

3. Look in the top row above the time signature to find the type of note that equals one beat.

	Simple time			Compound time		
Value of each beat (type of note)	𝅗𝅥 (minim)	𝅘𝅥 (crotchet)	𝅘𝅥𝅮 (quaver)	𝅗𝅥. (dotted minim)	𝅘𝅥. (dotted crotchet)	𝅘𝅥𝅮. (dotted quaver)
Value of each beat as a fraction of a semibreve	$\frac{1}{2}$	$\frac{1}{4}$	$\frac{1}{8}$	$\frac{3}{4}$	$\frac{3}{8}$	$\frac{3}{16}$
2 beats in each bar	$\frac{2}{2}$	$\frac{2}{4}$	$\frac{2}{8}$	$\frac{6}{4}$	$\frac{6}{8}$	$\frac{6}{16}$
3 beats in each bar	$\frac{3}{2}$	$\frac{3}{4}$	$\frac{3}{8}$	$\frac{9}{4}$	$\frac{9}{8}$	$\frac{9}{16}$
4 beats in each bar	$\frac{4}{2}$	$\frac{4}{4}$	$\frac{4}{8}$	$\frac{12}{4}$	$\frac{12}{8}$	$\frac{12}{16}$

ITALIAN TERMS

A tempo Resume the normal speed.
Accelerando Becoming gradually faster.
Adagio Slow, leisurely.
Agitato Agitated.
Alla marcia In the style of a march.
Allargando Broadening out.
Allegretto Slightly slower than Allegro.
Allegro Lively, reasonably fast.
Andante (lit. walking) At a moderate pace.
Andantino A little andante.
Animato Animated.
Cantabile In a singing style.
Con With.
Crescendo *(cresc.)* Becoming louder.
Da Capo (D.C.) al Fine Back to the beginning and finish at the word Fine.
Dal Segno (D. S.) From the sign 𝄋
Deciso Decisively, firmly.
Diminuendo *(dim.)* Becoming gradually softer.
Dolce Sweetly.

E, Ed And.
Espressivo *(espress.)* With expression, with feeling.
Forte (f) Loud.
Fortissimo (ff) Very loud.
Grazioso Gracefully.
Giocoso Humorously.
Largo Slow and stately, broad.
Larghetto Less slow than Largo.
Legato Smoothly.
Leggiero Lightly.
Lento Slowly.
Maestoso Majestically.
Meno mosso Less movement.
Mezzo forte (mf) Moderately loud.
Mezzo piano (mp) Moderately soft.
Moderato Moderate time.
Molto Much.
Moto Movement.
Non troppo Not too much.
Pianissimo (pp) Very soft.

Piano (p) Soft.
Più mosso More movement, quicker.
Poco a poco Little by little (gradually).
Pomposo Pompously.
Presto Very quick.
Quasi As if, almost.
Rallentando (rall.) Becoming gradually slower.
Ritenuto (rit.) Hold back (slower at once).
Rubato Flexibly.
Semplice Simple.
Sempre Always.
Sforzando (sf , sfz) Forcing, accented.
Solenne Solemn.
Sonore Sonorous, full toned.
Sostenuto Sustained.
Spirito Spirit, life, energy.
Tempo I Resume the original speed.
Tenuto Held.
Tranquillo Quietly.
Un poco A little.
Vivace Lively, quick.

Printed by
Halstan & Co. Ltd., Amersham, Bucks., England